I'm Brave

By Pauline Cartwright

I'm not scared
of spiders.
I'm brave!

I'm not scared
of dragons.
I'm brave!

3

I'm not scared
of climbing trees.
I'm brave!

I'm not scared
of the dark.
I'm brave!

I'm not scared
of dogs.
I'm brave!

I'm not scared
of water.
I'm brave!

But I don't like
fuzzy, buzzy **moths!**

8